Russ Abbot's Fun Book

Cooperman's Box of Tricks

1	12	32	14	25	6	21	19	8		
11	33	39	20	2	36	29	31	18	30	
24	17	5	26	9	13	38	4	37	28	
10	34	23	3	15	35	22	40	16	27	7

'Where shall we (36,20) on holiday this year?' asked Blunderwoman.

'I'm not going (29,8,32,32,2,36) again – the snow was too (12,30,1),' said Cooperman.

'That was the beach, you plonker,' said Blunderwoman.

'I wondered why I was the only one wearing a bobble hat.'

'I had a jolly old (39,21,19,8) in this brochure,' said Boggles, who had just flown in, 'and they've got some lovely golden beaches.'

'That's not a brochure, it's a cookbook. You're looking at an omelette,' snorted Blunderwoman.

'I thought the temperatures were a bit (12,32,36,12),' laughed Boggles.

'Why don't we go to the end of the garden?' suggested Cooperman. 'It'll (6,33) nice and cheap there and everyone speaks English. Mind you, you never know what the food will be like!'

'(32,18,14) got to be better than here,' interjected Geronimo, who had just parked his skateboard on the tortoise.

'Let's (11,20,30,8) it up then!' suggested Blunderwoman.

Published by BBC Books
a division of BBC Enterprises Limited,
Woodlands, 80 Wood Lane, London W12 0TT
First published 1990

ISBN 0 563 36056 9

Designed by Hammond Hammond
Art Director: Roger Hammond

Printed in Great Britain by Cooper Clegg Web Offset, Tewkesbury
Bound in Great Britain by Butler & Tanner Ltd, Frome, Somerset
Jacket printed by Belmont Press Ltd, Northampton

THE WRITERS

All the material in this book has been adapted from the Russ Abbot shows on BBC television. The writers of the original scripts were as follows:

Fatman vs The Joker Barry Cryer and Dick Vosburgh

Twist in the Tale and *The Red-headed Mystery*
Paul Minett and Brian Leveson

Anthony's Devon Adventure Kim Fuller and Geoff Atkinson

Chute to Kill Peter Robinson and Peter Vincent

Reach for the Bucket Malcolm Williamson

The puzzles and games were devised by Joel Morris and Jason Smith

Von Meatball's Crossword was set by Peter Robinson

All other material by Barry Cryer and Peter Vincent

THE ARTISTS

Jacket artwork by Larry Rostant

Other illustrations by Carlos Ezquerra, John Stokes, Vicente Ibanez, Perez, Jordi Macabich, J. Garcia (all represented by Bardon Press Features Ltd), Chris Lloyd, Joel Morris, Larry Rostant and Peter Ross

PICTURE CREDITS

Front Cover © BBC (Boggles); TV Times (C.U. Jimmy)
Back Cover © BBC.

London Weekend Television page 36, 46, 61, 73 and 78;
TV Times page 39

All other photos © BBC.

FOREWORD

GREAT! Great! Oh aye, it's the most lummicky threadle booky treat the noo! Jings! Sling your sporran on the griddle and hooley awa wi' smashing stories, adventures and hoochy funnybone page tickles! Do I make masel clear?

Here's nutting you!

C. U. JIMMY

FATMAN
VS.
THE
JOKER

MID-AFTERNOON, THE WHITE HOUSE, WASHINGTON. THE PRESIDENT HAS A CRISIS ON HIS HANDS!
THE JOKER IS CRUISING OFF THE COAST OF FLORIDA IN AN ATOMIC SUBMARINE! HE THREATENS TO BLOW UP THE UNITED STATES, UNLESS WE PAY HIM A BILLION DOLLARS, PLUS V.A.T.!
WHAT ARE WE GOING TO DO, MR PRESIDENT?
BRING ME THE FAT PHONE!
HELLO, FATMAN? GET OVER HERE RIGHT AWAY!
EXCITING, ISN'T IT? I'M THE WHITE HOUSE MOUSE!
FATMAN'S ARRIVED, MR PRESIDENT! HE'S IN THE ELEVATOR IN THE BASEMENT!
WE HAVEN'T GOT A BASEMENT!
WE HAVE NOW!
GOOD AFTERNOON, MR PRESIDENT. I SHOULD HAVE HAD A FITTING FOR YOUR ELEVATOR.
REMEMBER THE RIDDLER, FATMAN?
YES, HE HAD A PROBLEM. BUT HE COULD WRITE HIS NAME IN THE SNOW.
WE DEFEATED HIM WITH THIS...
ON IT, YOU WILL FIND YOUR INSTRUCTIONS.
THANK YOU, SIR.
THAT TAPE WILL...
MMMM, DELICIOUS...
SELF-DESTRUCT IN 5 SECONDS.
MEANWHILE, THE JOKER WAITS FOR THE PRESIDENT'S REPLY TO HIS DEMANDS!
TODAY'S THE DAY! UNLESS THE PRESIDENT KICKS IN WITH THE DOUGH, BOOM!

THERE'S SOME LARGE CRAFT APPROACHING, BOSS!
WEARING HIS SCUBA MOUNTIE SUIT, FATMAN HEADED FOR THE SUBMARINE.
FATMAN! WHAT ARE YOU DOING?
ANY QUESTIONS?
HOW DID YOU GET HERE, FATMAN?
YOU'RE GONNA HAVE A FRONT SEAT WHEN I BLOW AMERICA TO KINGDOM COME!
BOSS, BOSS! WE'RE SINKING!
SINKING??
YES, WE'RE SINKING, BECAUSE I'M SO FAT, THE LAST TIME I SAW MY FEET I WAS WEARING BOOTEES!
POW!
WHAT AM I DOING HERE?
I'M SO FAT THAT WHEN I FALL DOWN, I ROCK MYSELF TO SLEEP, TRYING TO GET UP!
I'M SO FAT THAT WHEN I GO SWIMMING, PEOPLE SHOUT "SAVE THE WHALE!"
ZAP!
FATHOMS DOWN AND THESE JOKES!
WATER'S COMING IN THE SUB, BOSS!
THIS IS THE LAST STRAW!
LAST STRAW? THAT GIVES ME AN IDEA!

Are you sure this is Esther Rantzen's room?

CROSSWORD

SET BY

Dr Heinz von Meatball

Guten tag, mein eine kleine pumpernickels! Here iss mein Iron Crossword. It iss Krupptic – ja? You will be very much enjoying this Teutonic diversion – and that iss an order!

All ze clues are easy and all the answers are very difficult – Ha ha ha! Who says ve Germans don't hev ein sense of humour?

Furst korrekt solution to reach mein office vill be put on der couch and analysed!

Get to it, jungsters! Don't be afreud!

Clever vordplay. Ha ha ha!

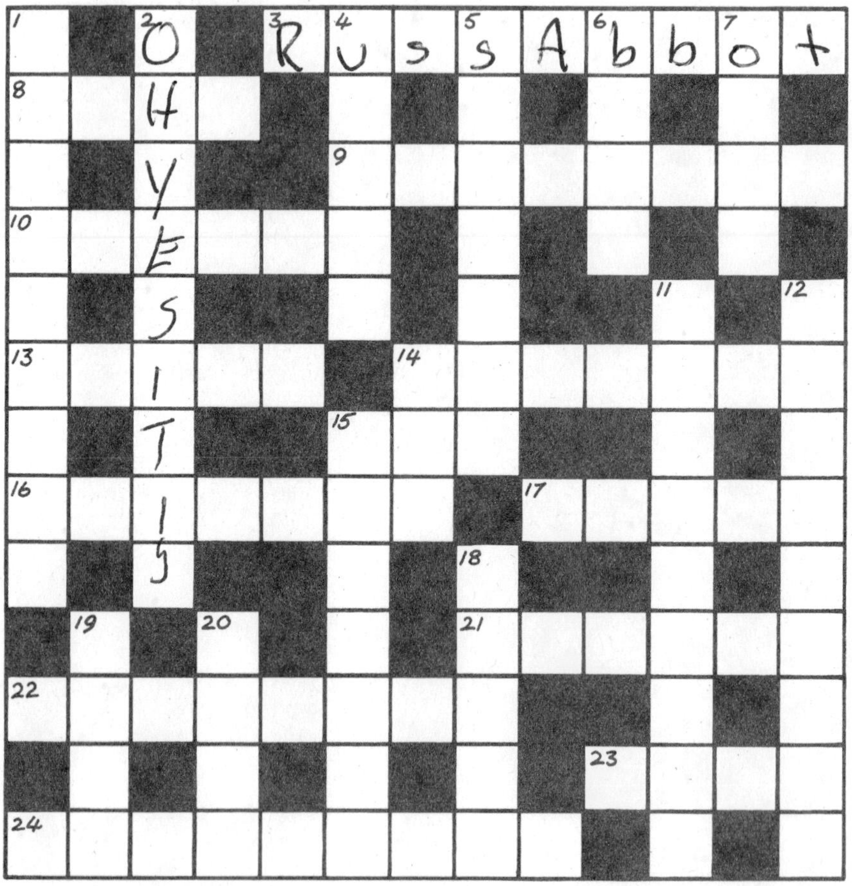

Clues

ACROSS

3 He'll make 'em laugh or bust ABs – being disorderly. **(4,5)**
8 Finish this to get the rum. **(2,2)**
9 (with 19 down) 008's pad. **(8,4)**
10 Barry Humphries might read a note thus addressed. **(2,4)**
13 Good tourist directions in Plymouth give you a lift. **(5)**
14 This ex-P.M. takes Urdu tea round. **(7)**
15 Either way it's still Help! **(3)**
16 Anger in confusion before entry for this town. **(7)**
17 & 21 Herb sounds imperfect hotelier. **(5,6)**
22 I'll be a good cub and . . . **(2,2,4)**
23 It's this to tell a lie in song. **(1,3)**
24 Just before Christmas with Midge for exciting experience. **(9)**

18 DOWN! jA, ALL RIGHT SMARTIE, ZE CLUE'S MISSINK. ZE ANSWER ISS "AFTER". Ach! Donner und Zeppeliss!

DOWN

1 All mixed up, this dry a.m. – You might say this about this clue! **(2,3,4)**
2 Oh no, it's not! **(2,3,2,2)**
4 Mixed up Eva of the town. **(5)**
5 They couldn't be called Bros if they were this. **(7)**
6 Secure the new order of The Blot. **(4)**
7 Rubik wasn't responsible for these. **(4)**
11 After boxing the compass, opening a raincoat makes an urgent announcement. **(4,5)**
12 Tony with cunning curiously deserves a sentence. **(6,3)**
14 Primitive thermometer used in bath. **(3)**
15 Advice to squirrel when confronted with nutcase. **(5,2)**
19 See 9 across.
20 Sounds like Nero wasn't telling the truth. He was on this – not the fiddle. **(4)**

Answers on p. 73.

ANTHONY'S DEVON ADVENTURE

FIRST
RIVETING
INSTALMENT

'Hello, 'I'm Anthony.'

'My name's Luthy.'

Anthony looked at the girl. She seemed a bit soppy, but there was a good chance they'd become chums and have some adventures together on this holiday in a country cottage in Devon.

'I'm staying with my aunt and uncle,' said Lucy, 'but it's not the same without Daddy. He disappeared in mysterious circumstances.'

'Golly,' thought Anthony, 'a mystery already! This is going to be a beezer holiday!'

'Anthony! Your dinner's on the table!' came Mum's jolly voice from the kitchen.

'What is it?'

'It's a wooden thing with four legs!'

'Oh *Mum*,' thought Anthony. Why were grown-ups always so embarrassing?

◆ ◆ ◆

'This is good fun. Where are we going?' Lucy's face was pink with excitement. They were in Keystone Copse, which ran down to the sea.

'Hear the waves?' said Anthony. 'They're surging into Smigglers Cove.'

'*Smigglers* Cove?' frowned Lucy.

'Yes, somebody spilled tea on the map!'

Anthony got his sense of humour from his mother.

'Reminds me of that poem,' said Lucy. 'I must go down to the sea again . . . to the lonely sea and the sky.'

'I've got some woollen swimming trunks . . . that shrink up when they're dry!' laughed Anthony.

'That's lovely!' chimed in Lucy.

'Not if you're wearing them, it's not,' added Anthony, drily.

◆ ◆ ◆

'Do you think Luthy's a silly name?'

Anthony thought: 'How strange she only lisps when she says Lucy!'

They had now reached the beach. The gulls squawked and the sea gave a long rumble. So did Anthony's tummy. Suddenly he stubbed his toe on something.

'Golly! What's this?'

'It's your toe, silly!'

'No, I mean this chest thing. Are you thinking what I'm thinking?'

'How should I know?' pouted

Continued on next page

Lucy. 'I'm not a mind reader.'

'You know what I'm thinking? *Smigglers* . . . I mean . . . smugglers.'

Feverishly, they tore the lid off the chest. The unmistakeable dull gleam of gold caught their eye.

'What is it, Anthony?' gasped Lucy.

'If I'm not mistaken, Lucy,' rasped Anthony, 'this is chocolate vanilla fudge.'

'How do you know?'

'Tell you later. Quick! Someone's coming!'

◆ ◆ ◆

The two chums scampered off and hid behind a boulder, their hearts beating wildly. Two rough-looking men were unpacking the chest.

'Crikey! Smugglers!' breathed Lucy.

'Yes,' replied Anthony, 'and we've got the evidence right here.'

Lucy couldn't hear him very clearly, as his mouth was full of fudge.

'This'll kill me if I eat any more,' groaned Anthony.

'*They'll* kill us if they find us!' Lucy's eyes were like saucers . . .

What a corking tale!
See page 27 for next instalment, pals!

ROAD SIGNS

Hello kids. Cooperman here. You're not driving yet, but when you do you'll see a lot of traffic signs. That is, if you're facing the front. Which, by the way, is a good thing to do when you're driving a car.

My second tip is always sit in the front seat. You'll be nearer the clock. And – if you want to know the time, it's half past three.

When I was a kid, I wanted to be a lollipop man. They don't start work till they're sixty. But how they lick those things, I'll never know.

Here's another tip. If you find yourself going the wrong way up a one-way street, make sure you're not in a car. Here's a funny thing. I was driving up a one-way street and a policeman said: 'Didn't you see the arrows?' I said: 'I didn't even see the Indians!'

Anyway, here are some road signs and what they mean. I'm off for a drive. I've got a daisy car. Some daisy goes and some daisy doesn't.

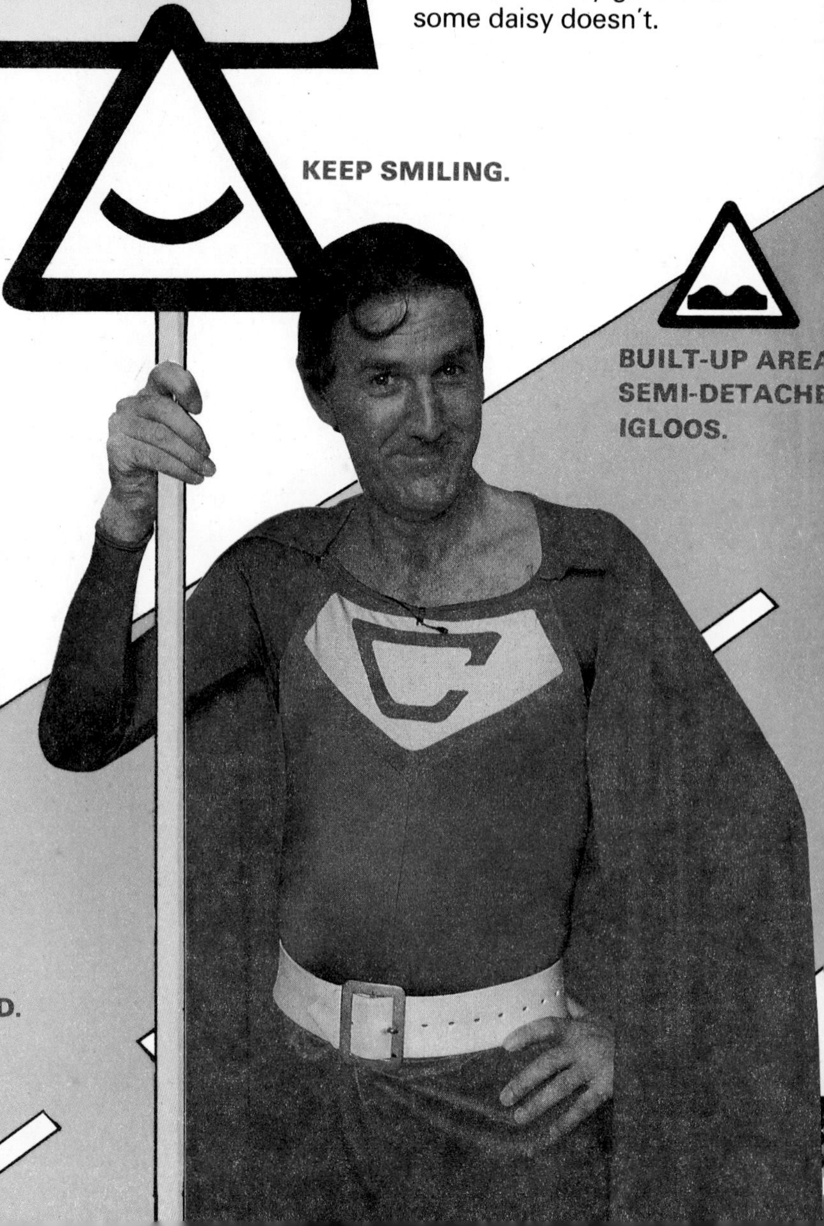

KEEP SMILING.

BUILT-UP AREA SEMI-DETACHE IGLOOS.

TUNING FORK IN ROAD.

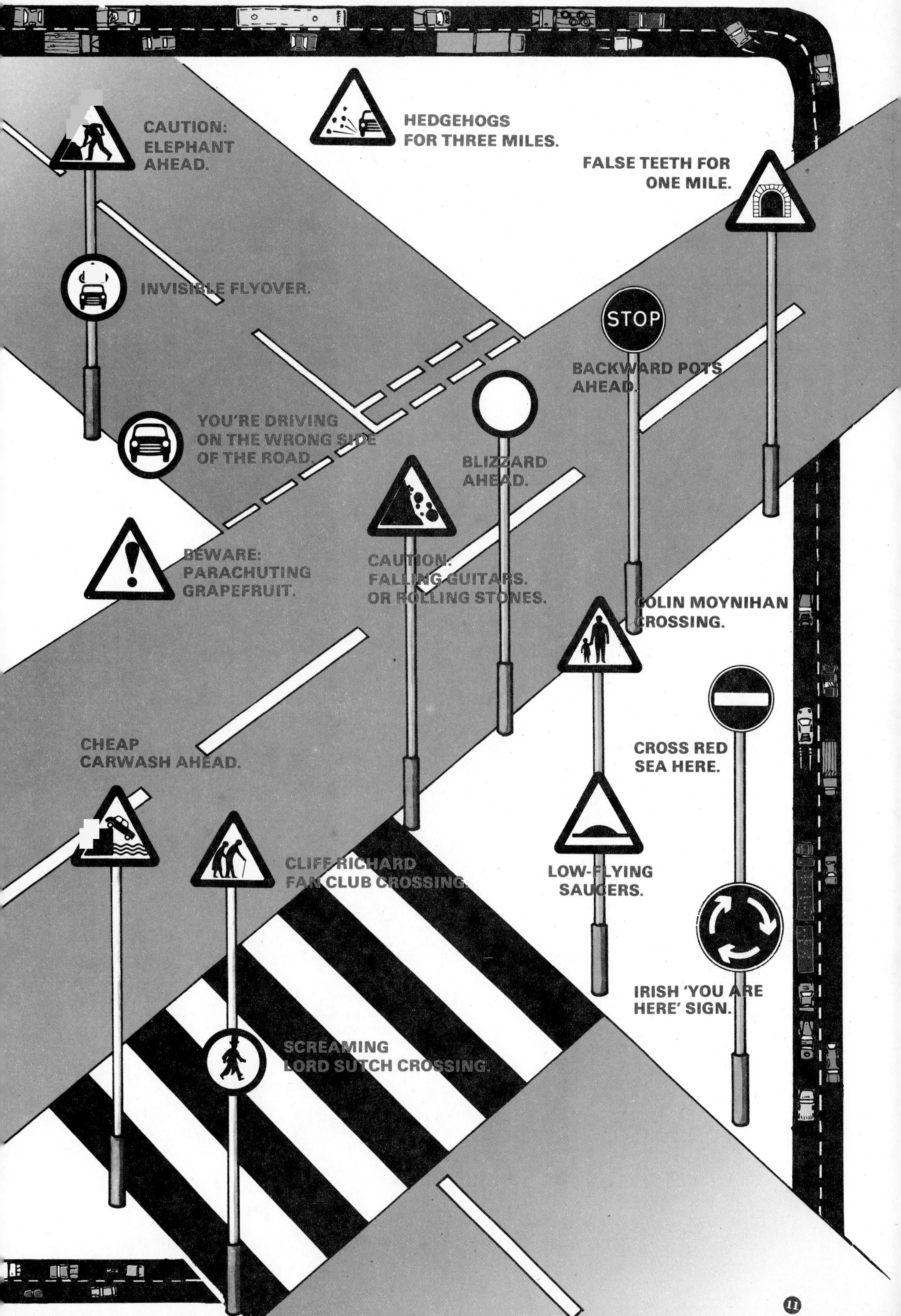
CAUTION: ELEPHANT AHEAD.
HEDGEHOGS FOR THREE MILES.
FALSE TEETH FOR ONE MILE.
INVISIBLE FLYOVER.
STOP
BACKWARD POTS AHEAD.
YOU'RE DRIVING ON THE WRONG SIDE OF THE ROAD.
BLIZZARD AHEAD.
BEWARE: PARACHUTING GRAPEFRUIT.
CAUTION: FALLING GUITARS. OR ROLLING STONES.
COLIN MOYNIHAN CROSSING.
CROSS RED SEA HERE.
CHEAP CARWASH AHEAD.
CLIFF RICHARD FAN CLUB CROSSING.
LOW-FLYING SAUCERS.
IRISH 'YOU ARE HERE' SIGN.
SCREAMING LORD SUTCH CROSSING.

The Fencing Master

ALWAYS CLEAN THE WEAPON. RULE ONE: NEVER FENCE WITH A MESSY BLADE.
LET'S GET IT RIGHT THIS TIME. WAIT TILL I SAY 'PLAY'.
I SAID WAIT!
YOU JUST MAKE DIFFICULTIES FOR YOURSELF.
LET'S SEE IF YOU CAN PARRY AN ATTACK... ON GUARD!
THAT'S A BIT BETTER. TRY AND SEE WHAT I'M DOING TO YOU...
FFFFFFT!
NOW WE'RE JUST BEING SILLY, AREN'T WE?
S-S-SORRY.
IF YOU'RE GOING TO LEARN SWORDSMANSHIP FROM ME YOU MUST BE SERIOUS.
I THINK I'LL FENCE LEFT-HANDED FOR A CHANGE. GIVE YOU A BIT OF A CHANCE. ON GUARD!

GERONIMO'S BLUE MING VASE

Geronimo can turn a vase into a mess in four seconds.

Can you turn the word **Vase** into the word **Mess** in four moves, changing one letter at a time? (Only real words please.)

Answers on page 77

JIMMY WORDSEARCH

Jimmy says: Oh, it's greet! Rully greet! It's a sort a' hid'nae wurds all scramblae jumblae in thus greet bug squeer. Aye, s'greet!

Translation: 'Oh, this is splendid! Truly splendid! Well, it would appear that a large number of Scottish-style words have been cunningly concealed in all directions within this generously large square. Quite magnificent!'

WORDS

- Angus
- Auld
- Bagpipes
- Ben Nevis
- Burns
- Caber
- Celtic
- Dram
- Gay Gordons
- Ginger
- Glasgow
- Haggis
- Hairy Knees
- Hamish
- Heather
- Hogmanay
- Jimmy
- Jock
- Kilt
- Lang
- MacJimmy
- Nessie
- North of Watford
- Porridge
- Rangers
- Sassenach
- Sporran
- Sword Dancing
- Syne
- Tartan
- Thistle

T	P	C	I	T	L	E	C	B	A	G	P	I	T	E	S
S	O	T	H	O	N	L	H	S	S	D	L	U	A	B	A
R	R	D	R	O	F	T	A	W	F	O	H	T	R	O	N
E	R	W	G	P	U	S	P	O	R	R	A	N	T	A	G
G	I	O	M	S	S	I	T	R	S	U	G	N	A	C	U
N	D	G	A	E	I	H	O	D	E	J	H	U	N	J	K
A	G	S	N	N	V	T	E	D	E	H	A	G	G	I	S
R	E	A	A	K	E	G	S	A	N	A	T	N	O	M	E
J	C	L	Y	R	N	Y	R	N	K	M	R	A	N	M	P
H	O	G	M	A	N	A	Y	C	Y	I	K	U	E	Y	I
A	M	C	L	E	E	L	G	I	R	S	L	L	S	H	P
G	O	A	K	H	B	E	N	N	I	H	N	T	S	E	G
G	P	B	R	E	G	N	I	G	A	A	T	N	I	K	A
I	R	E	B	D	R	U	G	N	H	R	L	J	E	S	B
B	U	R	N	S	M	S	N	O	D	R	O	G	Y	A	G
A	S	L	M	A	C	J	I	M	M	Y	T	H	O	S	F

ANSWERS ON PAGE 74

MILDEW'S

I am Chief Inspector George Corner, better known as 'Corner of the Yard'. When I run through my many cases I often fall over! Just my joke!

The case I want to tell you about today is the Morris Mildew affair – which came to be known as 'Mildew's Revenge'.

Morris Mildew

Morris Mildew's Diary

August 13th

Flew in from Australia. Bonzer flight. Got to know one of the stewardesses, name of Crimplene. Built like Ayres Rock with a voice to match. (Editor's note: Morris Mildew was Australian.) Anyway, here I am in the old country in a little village called Mildew Bottom.

August 14th (Paul Hogan's Official Birthday) I've decided to call on me old mum. My first home visit since she popped her clogs.

I've been looking again at the last letter she sent me. Nothing remarkable about it till you get to the end: 'P.S. Somebody's trying to kill me. P.P.S. I enclose a clean pair of underpants.' Then comes the bit that worries me: 'P.P.P.S. Hoping this finds you as it leaves me. Your ever loving – Aaaaaaaaargh!'

In all the time my mum's written to me she's never signed herself 'Aaaaargh!' I mean it's not a pet name or anything. I never called her 'Aaaaaargh'. I've got the feeling something could be wrong . . .

August 15th

I'm writing this in the graveyard right under the steeple of St Eeple in Mildew Bottom, a gloomy place made more depressing by the many graves that abound here. It didn't take me long to find the old lady's gravestone. It's a fair size and there's an inscription on it that reads as follows:

Here lies big-hearted Martha Mildew who died when she accidentally fell off the church steeple. Fell? Pushed more like! It would be just like the Mildew family to knock off the poor old cow and share out the estate. If you're reading this, Morris, you ought to do something about it and quick!

Revenge, Morris! Revenge is sweet! Must stop now as my tea is ready. Yours, a wellwisher.

REVENGE

When I first met Morris Mildew he made a deep impression on me. He was dead. But something caught my eye. Clasped in his rigid fingers was a diary. 'The Dennis Lillee Schoolboy's Diary'. This could tell me what I wanted to know! Namely – who killed Morris Mildew and five other members of his family over the course of three days! The entries that interested me began on August 13th . . . . (At this point the Inspector ran out of dots.) . . . . (Oh, he's found some more!)

I get the feeling that someone is trying to tell me something! I think I'd better call on my Great Uncle, Malachi Mildew. There's somebody knocking at his door! It must be me . . .

11 p.m. Having a lie down in the Limbo Bar of the Truss and Trumpet, Mildew Bottom.

It's been quite a day!
It wasn't far from the churchyard to the vicarage – about ten yards as the cow flies. (Shouldn't this be 'crow'? Ed.)

The Reverend Malachi Mildew had all the charm of a dead dingo in a dog collar. His study was full of bottles of poison. He would dip bread crumbs in it and leave them out for the birds. (Thought it was 'crows'. Ed.)

Eventually he suggested sherry. For a moment I thought he was going to offer me one. I wanted to ask him about Mum. I decided to approach the subject in a roundabout way. So I asked him – 'Did you kill my mother?'

His story was plausible. Too plausible. He told me Mum had fallen off the church steeple. At least three times. I smelt a rat. Then I saw it scuttling into the skirting board.

What was going on here? I asked him to show me the family portraits. The surviving members of the Mildew family had a certain charm – which escaped me entirely. I'd better make rough sketches of the portraits here so I remember them:

Cousin Mungo Mildew
Poacher, receiver of stolen goods, forger of luncheon vouchers and Magistrate

Uncle Montmorency Mildew
Lecher, cheat and drunkard. Master of Arts (Stolen).

Great Uncle Mordecai Mildew
Ruthless landlord, evictor of tenants (including his own daughter and baby into the snow) and greediest man in four counties.

Aunt Millicent Mildew
Malicious gossip, poison pen and blackmailer

The Reverend Malachi Mildew
Vicar, womaniser, embezzler, arch hypocrite and bird fancier.

If the gravestone was right, this gang of devious dingbats had put paid to my old mum. One thought occurs to me – What was she doing, writing a letter up on the church steeple? No matter! I knew pretty much what I had to do. While Malachi was chuntering on about the family – that chunderful charade of charmless charlatans – I realized two things. Firstly, I couldn't think of any more words beginning with 'ch'. Secondly I perceived either the Vicar or myself was about to snuff it – and I'd just decided that he'd volunteered.

I saw his sherry was running low so I topped it up from one of the poison bottles. Just as he was about to quaff the fatal flagon there was a burst of birdsong from the general direction of outside. I could have wrung that nightingale's neck! The old fool grabbed his shotgun and went walkabout in his wellies!

Bang!

That gun had a kick in it like a constipated kangaroo! The old fellow flew backwards into an open grave and there he lay like a boomerang in a billabong. Just to put the lid on it, a dirty great tombstone falls slap on top of him! The first do-it-yourself burial I've ever seen! Then the nightingale, who up to then hadn't given a 4X for anyone, did a 4X on him.

Well, he was dead – dead as a gecko in a geyser. And he never even touched the poisoned sherry!

One down and four to go.

Not a bad start!

And so to bed.

August 16th, New Moon. Koala Day

Dear Diary, I'm tucked up in bed here at the old T and T. It's been a real wombat of a day, frankly. At half past sparrow's fart this morning, I was out in the local bush, following the tracks of Mungo Mildew, the aforementioned poacher. Hardly needed the tracks, you could smell him for miles. He was the sort of joker, well, if you were around him, you'd use a pig as an air-freshener.

I had a little plan for Mungo, involving an exploding pheasant, a seesaw and a packet of Paxo stuffing, but as it turned out, I never needed it. There's a signpost down at Bellringer's Bog. One arm points to a local beauty spot and the other to the quicksands. I watched him through my Flying Doctor binoculars and as Mungo reached the signpost, I heard the sound of Constable Haywain's bicycle bell. He's the local bobby and I'd heard in the snug that the worthy P.C. had been following the putrid poacher, hoping to catch him in the act of stuffing a jumbuck in his tucker bag, pardon my French.

But Mungo heard the P.C.'s bell too; and quick as a funnel-web spider up a waste pipe, he turned the signpost round. Should I warn the stout custodian of the law that he was pedalling straight into a fiendish trap? While I was pondering on this point, over a few tubes of Ned Kelly's Bushwacker Lager, another figure made her appearance on the scene. I recognised the hatchet face and Dyno-Rod figure of Millicent Mildew, speeding along on her bicycle, scattering a group of Brownies on all sides. In no time, she'd overtaken Constable Haywain, sped past the signpost and was heading towards the bog. Should I warn her? Another diabolical dilemma.

Then I thought: 'Half a mo. Never look a gift bog in the mouth'. With a bit of luck and a following wind, the old girl would do the job for me. Die, that is. And so she duly did. I can still hear her angry cries as she sank beneath the festering slime of the bog. I closed my eyes in horror and took a short nap. When I opened them, only the partridge feather on her hat was visible. A sticky end indeed!

(Memo: Must buy some prunes. I won't say the food here's stodgy, but last night I broke a tooth on the custard.)

As if Millicent wasn't enough for one day, I had a beezer bonus. Mungo has a great big fridge outside his place, where he puts everything he's poached – eggs, salmon, you name it, sport. He was just slinging in the last brace of pheasant when his dog cocked the old leg against the door and shut it tight, with Mungo inside. His cries were pitiful. There was only one thing to do. I stuffed cotton wool in my ears. I couldn't believe my luck. The Mildews were dropping like flies. Three down and two to go. The end of a perfect day.

August 17th, Billabong Festival, New South Wales. If wet, Queensland

Mildew Hall, 2 p.m. I'm sitting here in the house of the late Montgomery Mildew, who has been dead for all of thirteen minutes.

And funnily enough, it was his birthday today. What could be more fitting than that his Australian nephew should bring him a lovely cake with one big candle? Though, I must confess, it was not so much a candle, more a stick of dynamite.

The way old Montgomery cashed in his corks was like this. I waited for the old drongo to get heaved out of his favourite watering-hole, The Lonely Skunk, a pub down in Little Fumbling. After a while, I heard the sound of his turbo Reliant Robin cannoning off the greenhouse and then I heard the sound of the door of the outside privy slamming shut. They say that the explosion that followed was heard from Milton to Keynes. I wouldn't know. All I do know is that they found his hat on a dredger in the Thames Estuary. He should never have had those eighteen pints and the three large vindaloos. Anyone want to buy some dynamite?

Four down, just one to go. All I've got to do is knock off old Mordecai and Mum can rest in peace. She will be avenged.

The Vicarage, 9 p.m. What a happy ending! I legged it up to Mordecai's farm. I made him a nice rhubarb pie. I didn't want to waste the dynamite. At first, all I could see was a party of nuns from the Little Sisters of the Really Broke and some destitute kids from the village, who were dressed in clothes made out of old copies of the Daily Mirror. They were having a picnic by the footpath and the nuns were just serving Kentucky Fried Reject Chickens and cardboard cups of water that they'd made fizzy by stirring it a lot. Suddenly, there was a bellow like a bilious bull and Great Uncle Mordecai was upon them, flailing away with an electric cattle prod. They all ran off as fast as their 39 legs would carry them and my revolting relative lost no time in stuffing himself with their Colonel Sanders cast-offs. Soon the heat of the sun overcame him and he fell into a deep sleep in the corn which, as I remember, was as high as a wallaby's eye. It was at that point that the combine harvester appeared. My course of action was plain. I sat down to watch. Isn't modern machinery wonderful? Within seconds, Mordecai had been bewildered, bundled and baled. He must have been the first man to be buried as a six pack.

It's peaceful here in my late Uncle Malachai's study as I sit thinking about all that's happened in the last three days. I haven't committed a single crime, I've seen my Mum avenged and I suppose I'll cop for the whole Mildew fortune. I think I deserve a glass of sherry and I'll toast the portraits on the wall. Absent friends!

Corner of the Yard here again. A strange tale and no mistake. What a plonker! He'd forgotten the sherry was poisoned. By him. Next year, I'll be presenting the case I like to call: 'Who killed Lady Soanleigh? The butler did'. I think you'll find it an intriguing mystery. Evening all.

(*Parrot adopts a woman's voice*)

'Monsieur Parrot,
There on the floor,
Father is dead.'
Fear not, my dear –
Parrot is here!
Little grey cells
Work it all out:
You did the crime!

(*Woman's voice*)
'But he's my dad!'

He changed his will!
Cut you right out!

(*Woman's voice*)
'Curses, I'm foiled!'

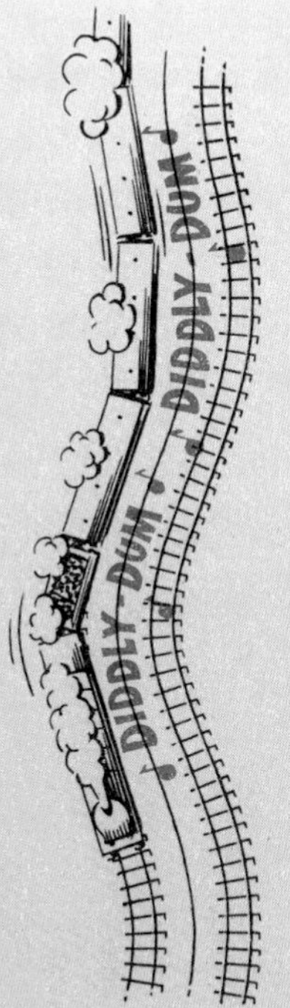

Take her away!
Hercule Parrot –
This is your life!

McBRIDE:
Now that we've met
Think I should say
Why I am here.
I heard a scream!

PARROT:
I did as well,
Madame Dubois!
She is next door.
Now we go in.
I smell a crime!

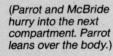

(*Parrot and McBride hurry into the next compartment. Parrot leans over the body.*)

PARROT:
Just as I thought!
Stabbed to the heart.
Also been shot.
Poisoned as well.

(*Picks up length of cord*)

Strangled with this!
Know what I think?
This is foul play!

McBRIDE:
Gad, what a brain!

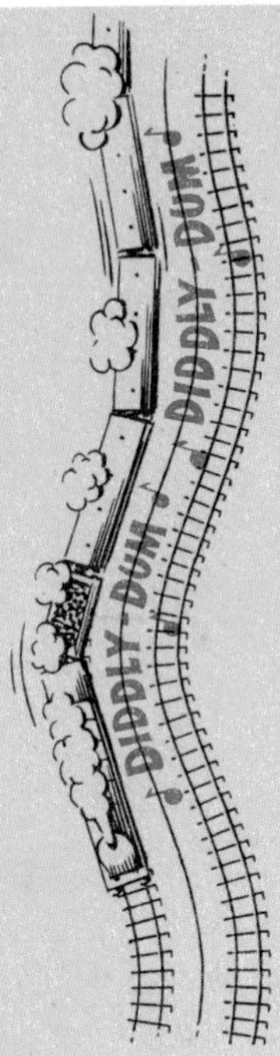

PARROT:
Killer is loose
Here on the train.

McBRIDE:
Killer is loose?
What shall we do?

PARROT:
Tighten him up.
Now I must think –
Who could it be?

(*He looks intently at the body*)

Why, what is this?

(*He picks up a diary*)

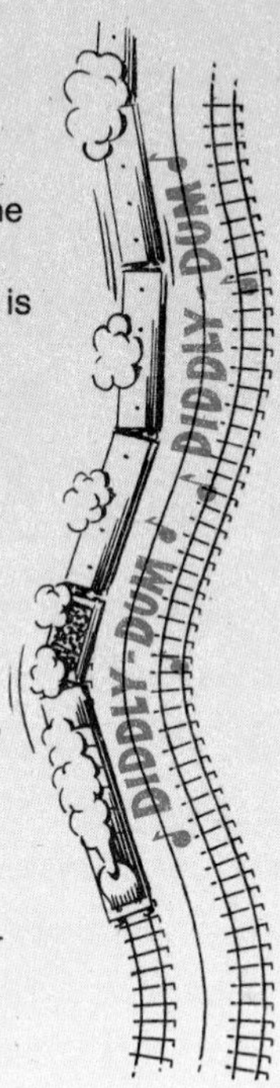

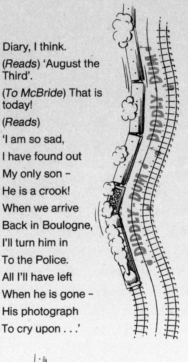

Diary, I think.
(*Reads*) 'August the Third'.
(*To McBride*) That is today!
(*Reads*)
'I am so sad,
I have found out
My only son –
He is a crook!
When we arrive
Back in Boulogne,
I'll turn him in
To the Police.
All I'll have left
When he is gone –
His photograph
To cry upon . . .'

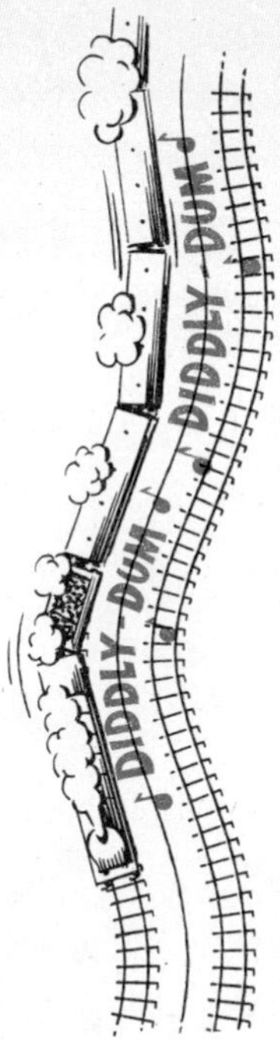

(*McBride twitches uneasily*)

PARROT:
If we can find
That photograph
Then we have found
Our guilty man!

(*He looks again at the body*)

Maybe it's there
Under the corpse.
Give me a hand.

(*They strain to move the corpse*)

McBRIDE:
Oh oh oh oh!

PARROT:
Are you all right?

McBRIDE:
Got a bad back . . .

PARROT:
You're not much help
Holding her down.
Leave it to me.
What's this I see?

(*He extricates the photo from under the body*)

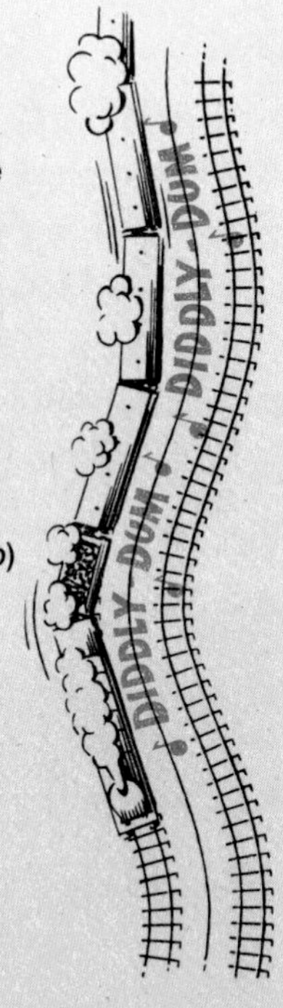

Just as I thought!
This is our man!
(*To McBride*) You are her son!
You killed your mum!

McBRIDE:
You have no proof!

PARROT:
(*Holding up the photo*)
Just look at this –
Little McBride
Taken at school
When he was ten!

McBRIDE:
Damn you, Parrot!
It's a fair cop!

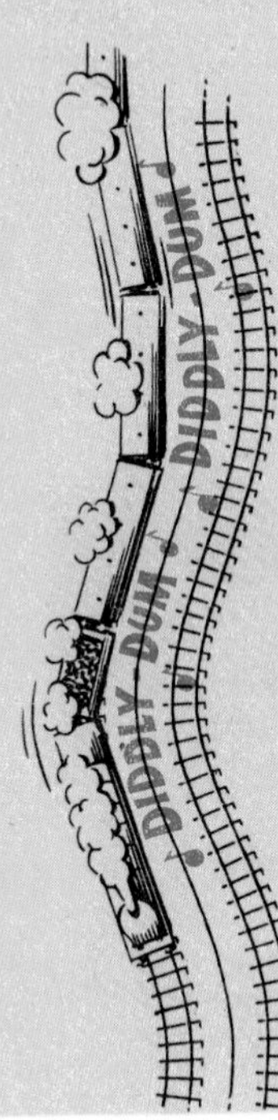

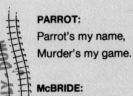

PARROT:
Parrot's my name,
Murder's my game.

McBRIDE:
You win this time,
Just not my day.

PARROT:
So much for crime.
Take him away!

CHUTE TO KILL
2,000 FEET OVER SALISBURY PLANE A BUNCH OF ROOKY RECRUITS PREPARE FOR THEIR FIRST PARACHUTE JUMP!
CARTER- JUMP! BLENKINSOP- JUMP! FULBRIGHT- JUMP! WHIMPOLE...
READY, SARGE!
HANG ABOUT. AS YOU WERE!
WHAT, SARGE? WHAT'S THE MATTER?
OH, DEARIE ME. WE'LL HAVE THIS OFF FOR A START!
RIGHT, THAT'S BETTER. CARRY ON, WHIMPOLE, JUMP.
SARNT!
ER... SORRY TO BE A NUISANCE BUT SHOULDN'T I HAVE A PARACHUTE OF SOME KIND?
GOOD THINKING, PRIVATE. YOU'LL GET ON! CAN'T USE THIS. PASSED ITS SELL-BY DATE – SEE?
LUCKILY I'VE GOT AN EMERGENCY CHUTE HERE.
WHAT'S THIS?
YOU'LL HAVE TO CLOSE IT TO GET IT THROUGH THE DOOR...
IT LOOKS LIKE A GOLF UMBRELLA.
CAMOUFLAGE, MY SON. IF THE ENEMY SEES YOU COMING DOWN WITH THAT HE'LL THINK YOU'RE MARY POPPINS.
BUT IT DOESN'T LOOK SAFE. WHAT IF IT BLOWS INSIDE OUT?
YOU CAN DIE CROSSING THE ROAD, CAN'T YOU, SON?

LOOK AT THIS... 'WATERPROOF' IF YOU LAND IN THE SEA YOU'RE LAUGHING.
I'M NOT HAPPY, SERGEANT...
IT'S NOT ME, SOMEHOW.
ALL RIGHT. I GIVE IN. HAVE A BLUE ONE.
I DON'T WANT A BLUE ONE. I WANT A PARACHUTE LIKE THE OTHERS.
WHAT PARACHUTE HAS A TONY JACKLIN AUTOGRAPH ON IT? ALL RIGHT. HERE YOU ARE. OUR LATEST MODEL.
HOLD IT OVER YOUR HEAD, STAND BY TO JUMP. THREE, TWO-
IT'S GOT 'WELCOME' WRITTEN ON IT!
WELCOME
AND YOU'RE WELCOME TO JUMP. STAND BY-
BUT IT'S A DOORMAT!
THAT'S MARSHLAND DOWN THERE! YOU'LL HAVE MUDDY BOOTS!
WHY HAVE YOU GIVEN ME A MAT?
BECAUSE I CAN'T GET A FLYING CARPET. ON YOUR WAY!
WHY CAN'T I HAVE A PROPER PARACHUTE?
WHIMPOLE, I'VE HAD IT UP TO HERE WITH YOU!
HERE YOU ARE THEN, LAST CHANCE! WHEN YOU LAND, BURY IT, THEY'RE SECRET.
I HAD ONE OF THESE WHEN I WAS LITTLE.
COURSE YOU DID! OFF YOU GO!
AND IN FUTURE, WHIMPOLE, I'LL THANK YOU TO TO KEEP AWAY FROM MY WIFE!

HOLMES

– THE SOLUTION!

'Elementary, my dear Armchair,' said Holmes, 'your stepdaughter stabbed Scrivens with a deer's antler. She was unobserved. On the face of it here was the perfect crime but she made several foolish mistakes. It is true that we found the footprints of a deer by the body of Scrivens but all the prints were made *by the same foot.* How many deer have you seen recently, hopping about the garden on one foot?'

'Very very few,' agreed Lord Armchair gruffly.

Holmes played a thoughtful cadenza on his magnifying glass.

'Your stepdaughter is a collector of animal exotica. She has a locked box in her room. When you open it, you will find, if I'm not mistaken, a deer's foot. While she was having a fainting fit I took the precaution of sucking out some fur through the keyhole by means of a milk straw.

'But Fiona's most stupid mistake was to claim that she was a hay fever sufferer. Granted, her eyes were watering but the smell of onion I detected when I entered her room suggests the pathetic means whereby she affected that little ruse.

'Consider this: would a hay fever sufferer keep a window box full of flowers in summer? Would a true sufferer from that unfortunate allergy keep her French windows open in mid-June? I think not. The fact is, your stepdaughter has an insatiable appetite for teeth. Scrivens possessed a flawless set of dentures which she had long coveted. After running from the scene of her crime, her first act was to clean those false teeth with her toothbrush whereas denture wearers do not use conventional toothpaste.'

'Just one thing, Holmes,' observed Lord Armchair, 'while you were talking I couldn't help noticing Fiona leaving the house with a packed bag . . .'

'Indeed,' pursued Holmes, unruffled. 'She is making for the station where she will be welcomed by Inspector Lestrade and his trusty sergeant.' It must be confessed there was a certain unbearable smugness about Holmes's tone.

'Damn you, Holmes,' snarled Lord Armchair. His face had changed and his accent had moved several hundred miles to the East.

'I thought so,' said Holmes, 'Professor Moriarty, I presume?'

'The same,' purred his arch opponent!

But that, chums, is another story . . .

ANSWERS TO PICTURE POSERS

1 Witches' convention in quicksands.

2 Black giraffe passing porthole.

3 Seagulls in tight formation.

4 Cyrano de Bergerac meets Barry Manilow.

5 Long John Silver's footprints.

6 Snorkelling dromedary.

7 Fairy struck by lightning twice.

8 Climax of Indian rope trick.

9 Pig leaving room.

10 Midget witness giving evidence.

11 Red Indian with hiccups behind hill.

12 Queen meeting world's tallest man.

13 Rabbits' balancing act.

14 Snail peering over TV set.

15 The End.

SCORES

If you scored nought, you are normal. Marry Kylie Minogue and retire immediately. FOR GIRLS: Ditto Michael J. Fox and/or Wet Wet Wet.

1–10 You have a strange outlook on life, but it's probably harmless.

11–14 See your optician *immediately.*

15 You are either a liar or a friend of the authors. As the authors have no friends – you're a liar!

Julio Doubleglazias

This song, sung by Julio, came 37th in the Eurovision Song Contest in 1937, after a recount.

There was a young boy of Macedonia
Who said to his girl: 'Tomorrow I'll phone ya'
But his phone was cut off
Because he hadn't paid the bill
Seventeen years she waited until
The phone suddenly rang
And her heart went 'Bong bing a bing bang'
She lifted the phone and said: 'Hello'
A voice said: 'Is that the Chinese take-away?'
And she said: 'No'
So much for love!

Oh Deirdre, I want you for my wife.

What's your wife going to do with me?

Eee, women!

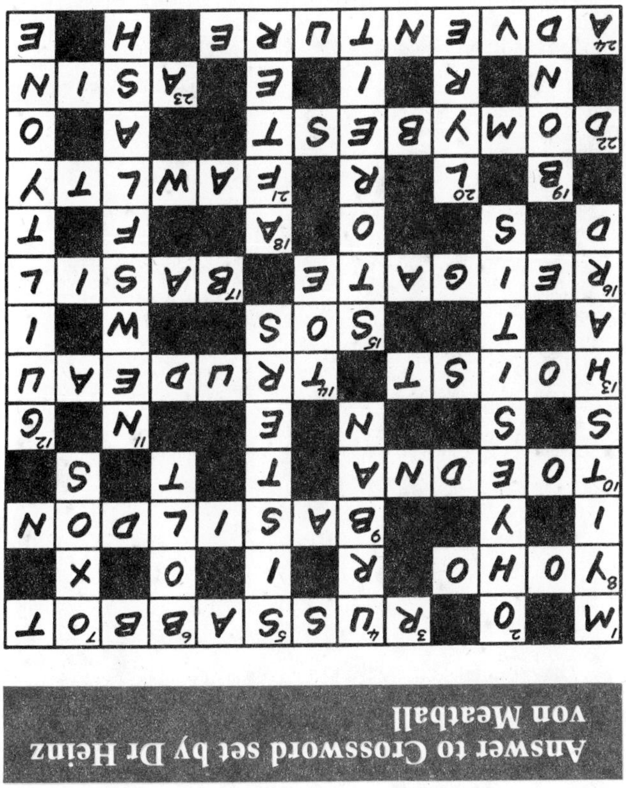

Answer to Crossword set by Dr Heinz von Meatball

Answers to Jimmy Wordsearch

T	P	C	I	T	L	E	C	B	A	G	P	I	T	E	S
S	O	T	H	O	N	L	H	S	S	D	L	U	A	B	A
R	R	D	R	O	F	T	A	W	F	O	H	T	R	O	N
E	R	W	G	P	U	S	P	O	R	R	A	N	T	A	G
G	I	O	M	S	S	I	T	R	S	U	G	N	A	C	U
N	D	G	A	E	I	H	O	D	E	J	H	U	N	J	K
A	G	S	N	N	V	T	E	D	E	H	A	G	G	I	S
R	E	A	A	K	E	G	S	A	N	A	T	N	O	M	E
J	C	L	Y	R	N	Y	R	N	K	M	R	A	N	M	P
H	O	G	M	A	N	A	Y	C	Y	I	K	U	E	Y	I
A	M	C	L	E	E	L	G	I	R	S	L	L	S	H	P
G	O	A	K	H	B	E	N	N	I	H	N	T	S	E	G
G	P	B	R	E	G	N	I	G	A	A	T	N	I	K	A
I	R	E	B	D	R	U	G	N	H	R	L	J	E	S	B
B	U	R	N	S	M	S	N	O	D	R	O	G	Y	A	G
A	S	L	M	A	C	J	I	M	M	Y	T	H	O	S	F

Did you score 32? Yer fleabit faker!

There's only 31. Use ya heid or ah'll use mine!

28–30 Great!

27 or less Awae hame ya English sassenackers!

'A gorilla went into a pub and ordered a pint. And the barman thought: 'What does he know about prices'. So he charged him five pounds. The gorilla stood there, sipping his pint. The barman, just to make conversation, said: 'We don't get many gorillas in here'. And the gorilla said: 'I'm not surprised with beer at five pounds a pint'.

ANSWERS TO 'IN THE THICK OF IT'

The letter is G

THE OBJECTS ARE:

Galleon
Gallows
Galoshes (gumboots)
Gargoyle
Gate
Gauntlet/glove
Geranium
Gerbil/guinea pig
Germany (on map)
Ghost
Giraffe
Girder
Glasses
Glider
Globe
Glockenspiel
Glove puppet
Glow-worm
Glue
Gnome
Gnu
Goalposts
Goblet
Go-kart
Golf clubs
Gondola
Graffiti
Gramophone
Grandad
Grapefruit
Grapes
Graph
Gravestone
Guardsman
Guillotine
Guitar
Gun

(The Thicks hid the brontosaurus behind the gerbil as it didn't begin with G.)

EAST SIDE STORY
ON THE THIRD FLOOR OF A PEELING TENEMENT BUILDING IN NEW YORK'S CRUMBLING LOWER EAST SIDE, A DESPERATE MAN DEFIES THE POLICE!
LET ME SPEAK TO THE BOY. LET ME SPEAK TO HIM. I KNOW THE BOY!
WHO LET HIM THROUGH?
IT'S ALL RIGHT. I'M THE BOY'S PARISH PRIEST. LET ME HAVE THAT MEGAPHONE.
JIMMY! CAN YOU HEAR ME, JIMMY? IT'S FATHER O'SHAUGHNESSY. I KNOW YOUR PARENTS, JIMMY. I KNOW YOU'RE A GOOD BOY, JIMMY!
JIMMY! I UNDERSTAND YOUR NAME IS BILLY. I'VE COME TO THE WRONG SIEGE, BILLY. SORRY ABOUT THAT...
BILLY, YOU KNOW ME... OH NO, YOU DON'T, DO YOU? I'M FATHER O'SHAUGHNESSY, BILLY. HELLO. NOW WE'RE FRIENDS, WILL YOU THROW DOWN YOUR GUN AND GIVE YOURSELF UP?
BILLY, I UNDERSTAND YOU'RE BEING HELD HOSTAGE BY LEFTY THERE, AND I SUPPOSE, REALLY, I SHOULD TALK TO HIM. HELLO, LEFTY, I'M FATHER O'SHAUGHNESSY...
LEFTY, I UNDERSTAND YOU'RE LEFTY, THE MAD PRIEST-KILLER. WELL, THIS IS RABBI O'SHAUGHNESSY AND I'M HERE TO HELP YOU. NOW NO ONE HAS BEEN HURT SO FAR, LEFTY.

Answers to 'The Mind Boggles'

1 He only took a photograph of her, didn't he?

2 It's the plug in the sink, isn't it?

3 The presents were helium filled balloons. When he'd got a certain number he naturally floated away.

4 He's an astronaut on the Moon. So the water freezes.

5 The package contains a parachute which failed to open.

6 He's a dwarf and can't reach the button for the seventh floor.

7 They've been scuba diving and decide to go back to the surface.

8 The well is 250 feet deep.

9 The surgeon is his mum.

10 Tricky one, this. The man is a mariner. On their voyage the ship was becalmed and the engine broke down. They were starving. One day the cook served roast albatross. The man ate it heartily. But his best friend had disappeared. He began to wonder what it was they ate . . .

When he came ashore he went straight to a restaurant and tasted roast albatross. But that's *not* what he had tasted on the ship. Oh dear, oh dear . . .

SOLUTION TO GERONIMO'S RATHER CROSS WORD

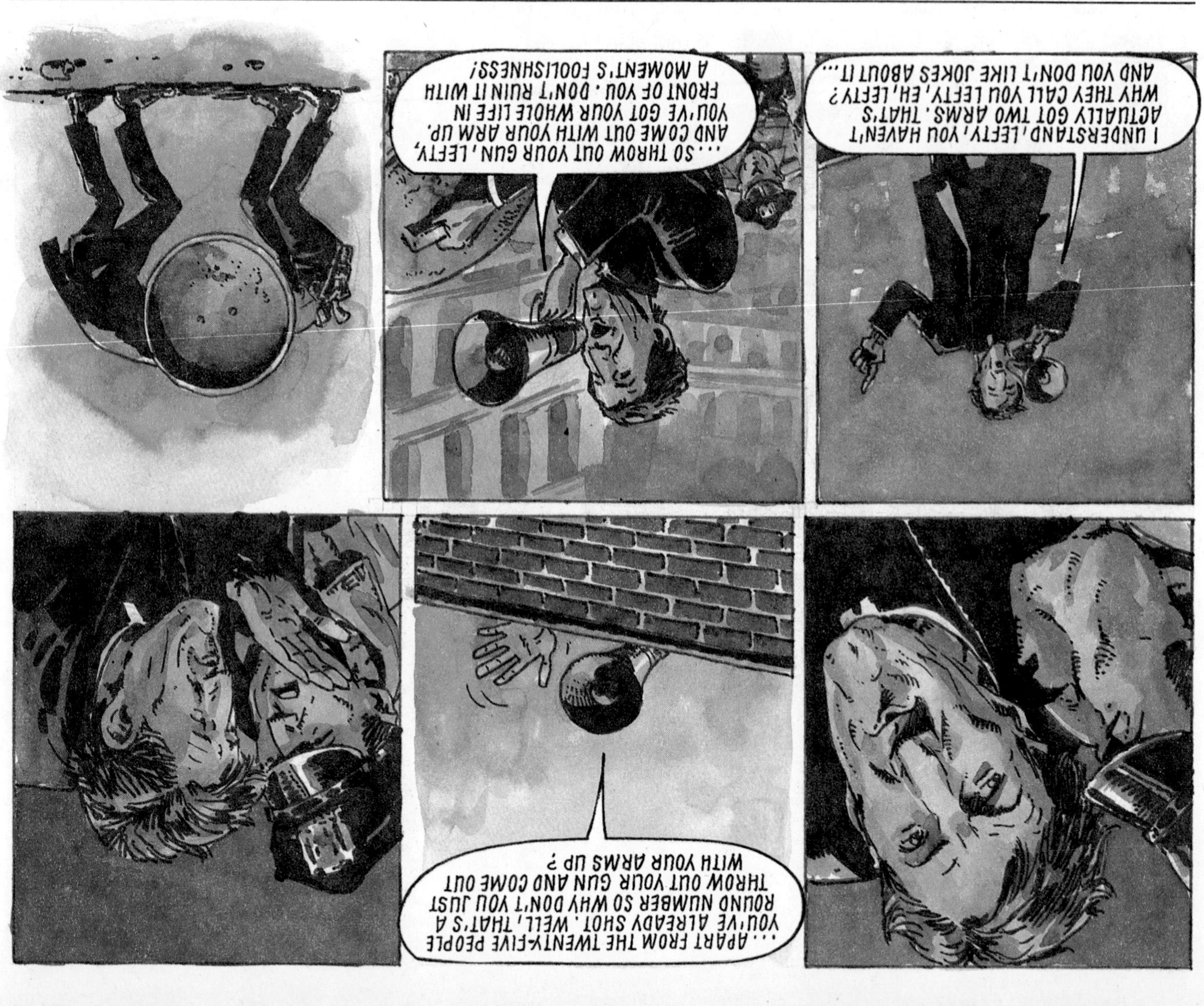

What do you get if you cross me with the river that runs through Newcastle?

I don't know. What do you get if you cross you with the river that runs through Newcastle?

Turpintyne! Give us your money!

ANSWERS TO SPOT THE DIFFERENCE

1 Mountie's jacket pocket has changed shape
2 Bangers and mash has become bananas and mash
3 The shack has a different chimney
4 The canoe in the bottom left has turned into a submarine
5 The letters on the saddle have changed
6 The tassel on the saddle has become a bell
7 The aeroplane is now a strange flying gentleman
8 The dark pine tree on the left has gone
9 The medals have gone
10 The burger has vanished
11 Tom now has an 'R' on his right boot
12 The horse has turned into a camel

Answer to Geronimo's Blue Ming Vase.

Vase–vast–mast–mass–mess

ANSWER TO 'THE MAN WITH NO NAME':

The answer is (e) – Russ Abbot.
(This was a trick question.)

1 His real name is Barrett Holmes.

2 **He's never been married but was once engaged in a phone box.**

3 He wears a size 9 shoe on his left foot and a size 11 shoe on his right foot, to fool his enemies into thinking they are following two one-legged men. He also wears them backwards, to fool them into thinking he's going the other way.

4 **He met Dr Watson through computer dating.**

5 His Stradivarius violin is centuries old, but he hopes to trade it in for a new one.

6 **He is standing on the cat. (Bet you didn't know that.)**

20 *THINGS YOU NEVER KNEW ABOUT...* BARRETT HOLMES

7 His address is 221b, Baker Street. 221a, downstairs, is occupied by Mr and Mrs Moriarty. Holmes never borrows sugar from them, as it is usually poisoned.

8 **His favourite disguises include an old Chinese mandarin, a demented gorilla and Janet Street-Porter.**

9 He wears Norfolk Tweeds for fishing, with his flies behind his lapel. Therefore, he has to stand on his head when he goes to the toilet.

10 **His least frightening case was The Chihuahua of the Baskervilles.**

11 His most frightening case was The Strange Affair of the Fart in the Lift.

12 **His most embarrassing moment . . . (see No. 11).**

13 His favourite record is 'A Load of Old Cobras' by the Speckled Band.

14 **He once crossed the Alps with an elephant and got a mountain that never forgets.**

15 In his study, he has Lord Nelson's skull. And a small one, which is Lord Nelson as a boy.

16 **His most surprising moment was when he leaped on his penny farthing from an upstairs window and realised, half-way down, that the saddle was missing.**

17 His favourite dish is Mrs Hudson's Baked Beans (see No. 11).

18 **His second most embarrassing moment was when he examined the Darjeeling Ruby through his magnifying glass on a sunny day and set fire to his trousers.**

19 He and Dr Watson won the three-legged race at Queen Victoria's funeral.

20 **He is a keen hot air balloonist (see No. 11).**

RESCUE BOND
THE SOLUTION

Bond thinks fast. Risking all, he leans to his right and immerses the bowl of the pipe in the bubbling acid. This extinguishes the fuse. Then he carefully drips the acid from the bowl of the pipe onto the ropes that bind his hands.

As soon as the acid has burned through the ropes he throws the pipe through the porthole. Then, raising both arms, he catches the hundred pound weight as it falls.

Twisting his body violently, he hurls the weight into the tank, shattering it. The acid pours down into the aquarium. As far as the piranha is concerned, it's frying tonight!

008 now addresses the parrot. 'Who's a pretty boy then?' he enquires. 'Jason Donovan,' replies the parrot and, of course, drops the key from his beak. Bond catches the key and, leaning out of the path of the laser, he unlocks the padlock and releases his feet.

At this point he executes his master stroke. He takes the Silver Jubilee spoon from his pocket and reflects the laser ray onto the control panel of the boat, using the highly polished bowl of the spoon as a focusing mirror. This short-circuits the boat's electronic systems and it stops. Bond turns the laser onto the explosives. He has ten seconds to leave! The door is locked! 'Kill!' he shouts and the karate-trained parrot demolishes the door with one blow of his wing. Gathering up the miraculous bird, Bond dives into the sea.

The boat blows up. Dangerous fragments crash into the waves but Bond is swimming under water, breathing the air trapped in the feathers of the parrot. The parrot is holding his breath as taught in Kung Fu.

As Bond surfaces he is unconscious from exhaustion. But the squawking of the parrot alerts the Royal Yacht. Soon both are given hot baths, rum and sunflower seeds.

'Nice to see you again,' murmurs Princess M*****l of K**t.

'And you,' says the parrot . . .

ANSWER TO WHO SITS WHERE?

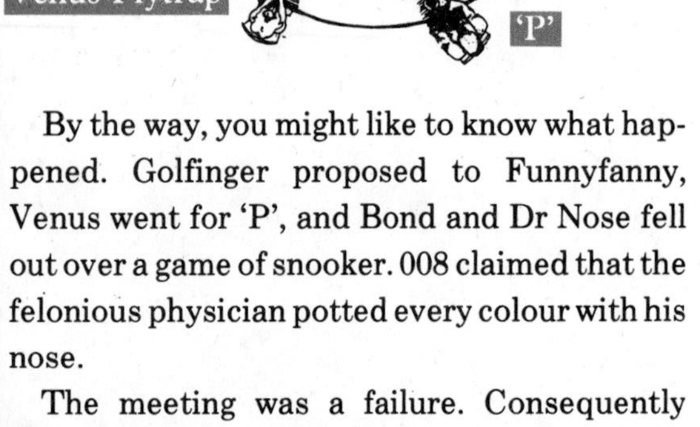

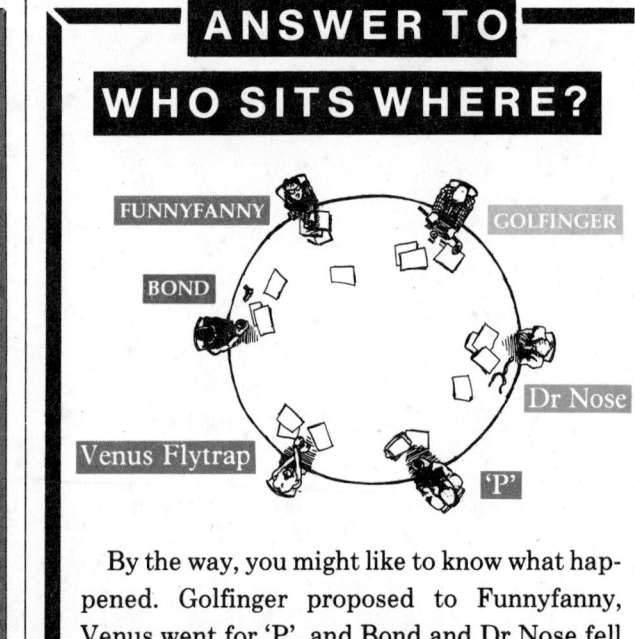

By the way, you might like to know what happened. Golfinger proposed to Funnyfanny, Venus went for 'P', and Bond and Dr Nose fell out over a game of snooker. 008 claimed that the felonious physician potted every colour with his nose.

The meeting was a failure. Consequently 'Kylie Minogue' now rules the world.

THIS BOOK HAS BEEN APPROVED BY THE MINISTRY OF FORWARD PLANNING

A LETTER TO RUSS FROM KYLIE MINOGUE

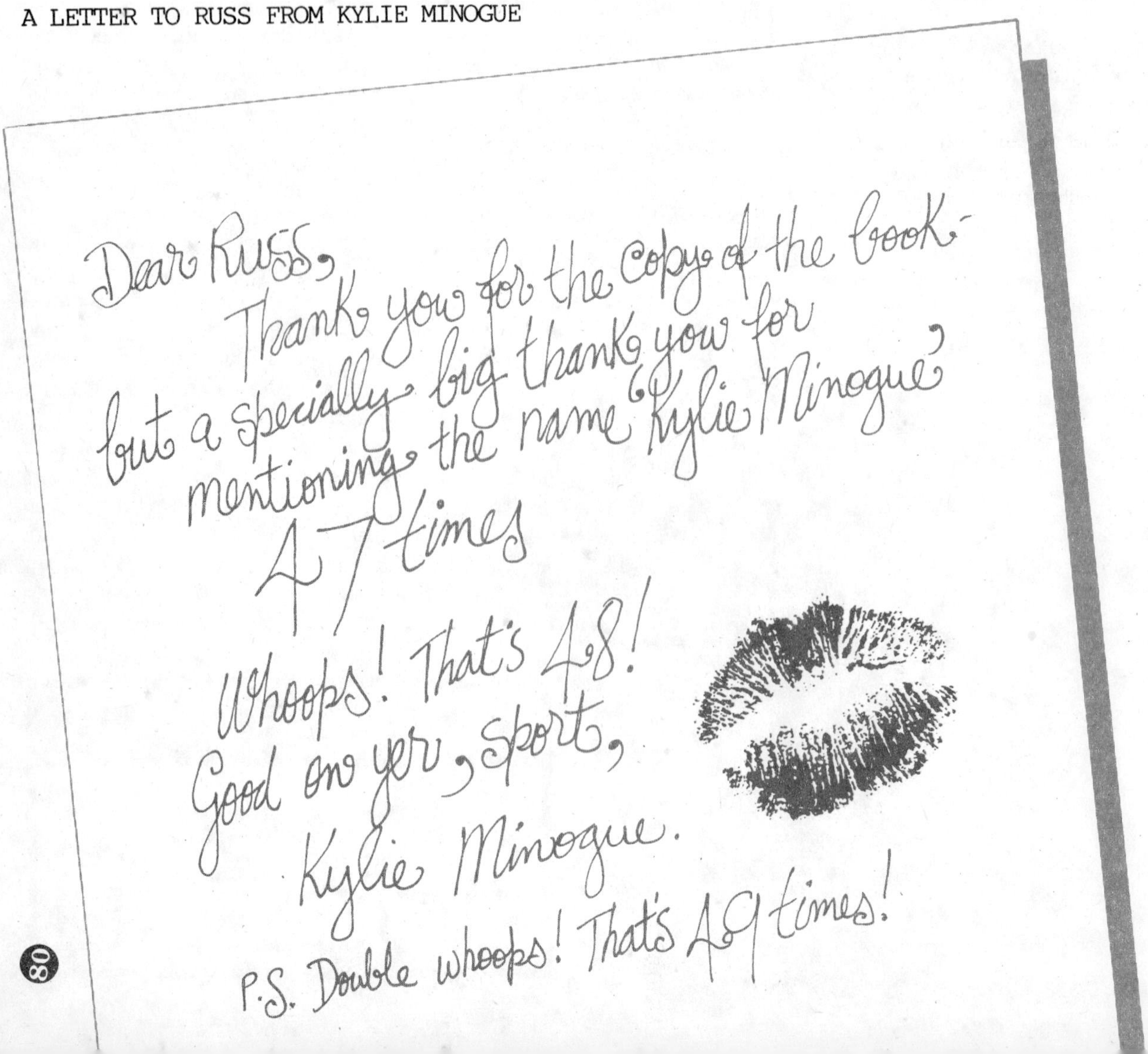

Dear Russ,
Thank you for the copy of the book-
but a specially big thank you for
mentioning the name 'Kylie Minogue'
47 times

Whoops! That's 48!
Good on yer, sport,
Kylie Minogue.

P.S. Double whoops! That's 49 times!